Travel Money, U.S.A.

by Margie Burton, Cathy French, and Tammy Jones

Dear Grandma and Grandpa,

We are going across the U.S.A. It will be a fun trip.

Today we went to the zoo. This was the biggest zoo that I have ever seen. It had so many animals! We did a lot of walking.

Love,

Jay

How much were peanuts at
the San Diego Zoo?

Dear Grandma and Grandpa,

    We went for a ride on the bus across this long bridge. It was fun! Look at all the wires on the bridge. They hold up the bridge.

                Love,

                Jay

How much was the bus ride across
the Golden Gate Bridge?

Dear Grandma and Grandpa,

    We stayed in the car as we went through this park today. We saw so many animals and some hot springs.

              Love,

              Jay

How much was it to get a postcard at Yellowstone Park?

Dear Grandma and Grandpa,

Look at this big, big rock. It is very, very old. We walked down to the bottom. It was a long way to walk!

Love,

Jay

How much was it to get down the Grand Canyon trail?

Dear Grandma and Grandpa,

Today we went to a cave.
We did a lot of walking
and climbing in the cave.
It was a long way down.
The cave is very deep.

Love,

Jay

How much was it
to go down in
Mammoth Cave?

Dear Grandma and Grandpa,

Look at this big waterfall.
We walked to the bottom
of the waterfall. It was
a long way to walk.

Love,

Jay

How much was it
to walk to
the bottom of
Niagara Falls?

Dear Grandma and Grandpa,

Look at this! We went to the top. We walked up so many stairs. It was a long way to the top of the crown.

Love,

Jay

How much was it to go to the top
of the Statue of Liberty?

Dear Grandma and Grandpa,
Can you send me some
more money?

Love,

Jay

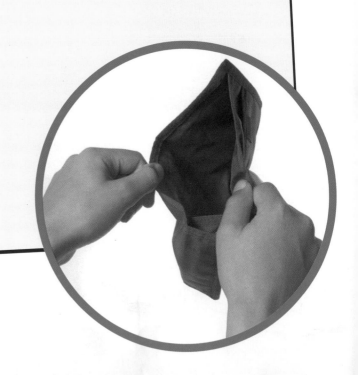